Preface

There are six Wide Range I
used alone or with Wide Rang_
with which they are parallel. The controlled voca__
graded sentence structure makes them suitable for children
with the following reading ages:

7 to $7\frac{1}{2}$ years	– Book 1
$7\frac{1}{2}$ to 8 years	– Book 2
8 to $8\frac{1}{2}$ years	– Book 3
$8\frac{1}{2}$ to 9 years	– Book 4
9 to 10 years	– Book 5
10 to 11 + years	– Book 6

The success of Wide Range Blue and Green Books has
been proved through the years, and the author hopes that
the addition of the Red series will bring pleasure to teachers
and children.

Phyllis Flowerdew

Contents

The Gilling Sword

This is a true story.

It all started with the tadpoles. They were swimming in a glass tank on a table in the classroom. Their legs were growing strong and frog-like. Their tails were growing shorter. Someone said,

"They'll be turning into frogs in a few days."

"Yes," agreed the teacher. "We'd better send them back to a pond when we break up."

"I'll take them," said Gary Fridd. He was nine years old, and he knew just the place for the tadpoles. It was a stream called Gilling Beck. It flowed through the fields very near his home. It bubbled and danced over the stones. It sparkled with specks of sunlight, or grew dark and grey with the shadows. Once there had been a ford nearby – a crossing place where people and wagons had made their way through the shallow water for ages past. Gilling Beck would be just the place for the tadpoles.

A few days later the Easter holidays started. Gary carried the tadpoles home in a jam jar. Then the next morning he took them across the grass to the stream. He knelt down and tipped them gently into the water. They wriggled away at once, darting in and out among the weeds, hiding behind stones, drifting happily in their new world.

Gary took the jam jar home, but later on he went back to the stream. He wanted to see if the tadpoles were still there. He knelt down in the long grass and gazed into the water. No. He could not see any tadpoles. They must have swum away. He peered behind the stones. His eyes followed a small floating twig and a line of bubbles. No. No tadpoles. But what was that? He saw a strange shape on the bed of the stream. It looked like the handle of something – something made of iron or tin.

He pushed up his sleeve and put his hand in the cold water. He felt the object. It was hard. His hand curled round it just as a hand had been meant to do. It *was* the handle of something. But what? He pulled it a little so that he shook off some of the stones that were lying on it. It was a sword. It was an old rusty sword, nearly a metre long.

Gary pulled it out of the water and stared at it in

amazement. He wiped it on the grass. It was complete, unbroken. There were five bands of different metal round the hilt, and a pattern inlaid on the handle. The blade was a little uneven at the pointed end. It was dirty and rusty, but otherwise perfect. Gary curled his fingers lovingly round the handle and cut through the air with a swish. He had a short imaginary fight with an imaginary enemy. Then with shining eyes he took the sword home.

"Whatever have you got there?" asked his mother.

"A sword," said Gary. "I was looking for the tadpoles and I found a sword."

.   .   .   .   .   .

Gary had found the sword, so of course he thought it now belonged to him. No one would be likely to lose such a thing these days. It must have been lying in the stream for hundreds of years.

"*My* sword," he said. "Findings keepings." But things were not quite as simple as that. There is a law in Britain about treasure trove. If someone finds hidden treasure that no one else claims, then it belongs to the Crown. Was the sword treasure trove? Did it belong to the Crown? This would have to be decided at court.

Gary's mother and father thought the best thing to do was to take the sword to the nearest museum and leave it there until the matter was settled. The people at the museum cleaned it and polished it until even the old rusty blade gleamed a little. As for the five bands round the hilt, and the inlaid pattern on the handle, these were of silver. A little polish, a little rubbing and they shone as they might have shone when the sword was first made.

"It's a valuable thing," said the museum keeper. "It's a Saxon sword from the late ninth century or the early tenth century. Just think! It's a thousand years old! It must be worth five or six thousand pounds today."

"If it becomes yours, you'll be able to sell it," said Gary's father.

"I don't want to sell it," replied Gary. "I want to keep it."

Lawyers work very slowly, and it was not until the end of September that the question of Gary's sword came before the court at Richmond in Yorkshire. Gary told his story. He told how he had taken the school tadpoles to Gilling Beck at the beginning of the Easter holidays.

"Then I went back later in the day to see if they were still there, and I found the sword lying in the stream."

The local policeman told his story. He said the sword was found near Gilling Bridge where there had once been a ford. The bed of the stream had been cleaned during the winter.

"Perhaps the sword was disturbed then," he said.

An archaeologist told his story.

"There was a settlement at Gilling as far back as the sixth century," he said. "The sword is beautifully made and must have belonged to someone important – probably a chieftain. It might have been lost in a battle, or perhaps a winning tribe had thrown an enemy sword into the stream. Probably the peat in the water had kept it in good condition."

It seemed that the sword was not treasure trove after all. It had not been hidden by someone. It had simply been lost or left behind or tossed away.

"It belongs to Gary Fridd, the boy who found it," the court was told.

.   .   .   .   .   .

It must have been very hard for Gary to settle down to lessons during these months. The sword was left on show at the museum. Gary hoped to have it back and keep it himself, but his parents said,

"It's too valuable to keep at home. Besides hardly anyone would see it. It would be better to sell it to a museum. Then hundreds of people would be able to see it – and you'd have a nice sum of money to put in the bank."

A little sadly, Gary agreed. It seemed the sensible thing to do.

So, in April of the next year, almost twelve months after he had found the sword, Gary watched it being sold for auction in London. It was sold at Christie's where all sorts of precious things come and go.

"This Saxon sword. I am offered five thousand. Any advance on five thousand?" asked the auctioneer. Someone in the crowded room nodded.

"Five thousand five hundred. Six thousand. Six thousand five hundred. Six five. Seven. Seven thousand."

Gary leaned forward and did not miss a word. His eyes gleamed with excitement and interest. The bidding went up and up. He could hardly believe it. He wondered who the people were who offered such huge sums of money. Were they sent by museums or were they millionaires with their own private collections?

"Eight thousand. Eight thousand five hundred. Nine thousand. Nine thousand five hundred. Ten thousand. Any advance on ten thousand? Any advance on ten thousand?" Bang! The auctioneer's little hammer struck the table. The sword was sold for ten thousand pounds.

Afterwards people crowded round the small boy from Yorkshire.

"You're a rich young man now. What are you going to do with all your money?"

Gary smiled.

"I'm going to spend some on a bicycle and a metal detector," he said, "and put the rest in the bank."

"Very sensible. Very sensible."

Yes. It was very sensible, but Gary would rather have kept the sword all the same.

.   .   .   .   .   .

The man who had paid ten thousand pounds for the sword was in charge of the Yorkshire Museum in York. Ten thousand pounds was the very most he could offer, so he was very glad when the bidding stopped there. So the sword went back to Yorkshire where it belonged. It was put on show in a glass case with a label beside it saying,

---

The Gilling Sword
Anglo-Saxon Sword: 9th Century
found at Gilling West, North Yorkshire
by Master Gary Fridd
Purchased April 1977

Gary went back to Yorkshire too. He was tired after all the excitement. As soon as he had a little time to himself he went down to his favourite spot – Gilling Beck. He knelt down and gazed into the water as if he almost expected to see the sword still lying there. He wondered. It might have happened just like this.

A Saxon chieftain might have knelt on the bank to get a drink of water in his hands. His sword might have slipped from its scabbard and fallen into the stream. He might have had to make a hurried escape, intending to come back later. Or he might have had the sword knocked from his hand in battle.

Gary could see the Saxons and hear their hoarse cries. He wondered so much how the sword had come to lie in Gilling Beck a thousand years ago. He wondered and he wondered, but he would never know.

There was a little movement in the grass beside him. It was a frog. Gary grinned.

"Maybe you were one of the tadpoles who started it all," he said.

Deep is the Earth

Deep is the earth,
So who can know
How many underground
Rivers flow?

How many caves
With rocky walls,
How many underground
Waterfalls?

In how many lakes,
Hidden and dim,
How many underground
Fishes swim?

Down in the earth,
Dark and deep,
How many underground
Creatures creep?

Deep is the earth,
So who can know
What things are
        happening
    Down below?

The Horse on the Hill

How old was the white horse on the hillside? Nobody knew. It had been carved out of the green grass, so that the white chalky ground beneath could be seen plainly, even from far away. People said it must have been there for hundreds and hundreds of years. Some said it had been made by the first men who lived in the valley long ago. There was a friendly look about the white horse on the hill. Yet there was something a little strange and mysterious about it too.

Jacob's cottage was in the valley, and his front windows faced the hill. He and his wife and his four small children looked at the white horse every day of their lives. On sunny days it was smooth and white and clear, but on rainy days it was shadowy and almost grey.

At night when the moon shone, the white chalk gleamed and the horse looked so alive that sometimes the family half expected to see it leap off the hillside and gallop away.

In Jacob's time, life was quiet in the valley; and such things as motor cars had not yet disturbed the peace.

One night in the winter when the lanes were wet and muddy and the air was cold, the baby of the family became ill. She had not been well all day, and now she was crying and coughing, and gasping for breath. The other children were asleep, but Jacob and his wife sat up in the candlelight by the dying fire.

"If only the doctor lived nearer," said Jacob's wife.

"I'll go and fetch him," said Jacob. "We dare not wait till morning."

"It's such a long way for you to walk," murmured his wife. "Wrap yourself up warmly, and take the lantern."

So Jacob put on his coat and his boots, and pulled a woollen hat over his ears. He lit the lantern and walked down the garden path and through the small gate. He closed it behind him with a click and he turned his face towards the village. A gust of cold wind almost took his breath away.

"I'll have to walk fast," he thought. He was full of fears for the baby, and his nerves were all on edge. Every house was in darkness. But what was that? Something moved against the hedge. Jacob's heart beat loudly. Then he looked in amazement as a horse came stepping out of the shadows.

It was a big, white horse. It held its head proudly and gave a snort of greeting. Its breath formed little misty clouds in the cold air. It came and stood beside him as if waiting for him to leap on its back.

"And why not?" said Jacob to himself. "This is just

what I need. The horse must have strayed from one of the valley farms. I'll ride to the doctor's on it. Then tomorrow perhaps I can find out who has lost it."

He climbed on the gate and mounted the horse. No saddle, no stirrups, no reins. It did not matter. Jacob had often ridden bare-back on farms where he had worked. He clutched the horse's flowing white mane with one hand and held the swinging lantern in the other. The horse broke into a gentle trot. The sound of its hooves echoed through the quiet night. Clip clop, clip clop.

Up the muddy lane trotted the horse, splashing through the puddles, sending mud and water flying. Soon it reached the high road. It was drier, harder than the lane, and now the horse changed to a gallop.

"This is fine. I shall be there in no time," thought Jacob. "Steady old boy, steady."

Soon the horse was galloping so fast that Jacob had to lean forward and clutch at the mane with all his strength. The lantern swung wildly and sent leaping patterns of light over the hedges. The horse galloped on and on, fast as the wind. Hedges, trees, and lonely cottages seemed to speed by. A duck on a wayside pond awoke and gave a small quack of surprise. A startled owl flew like a white ghost across the road.

Now the village came in sight. The houses huddled together in the darkness. The church tower stood like a black shadow reaching up to the sky. The horse's hooves clanged and echoed up the narrow streets.

There was the doctor's house.

"Whoa, whoa!" cried Jacob. He brought the horse to a stop. He had nothing to tether it with, so he took it to the side of the house and said hopefully,

"Wait there. Good boy."

Then to himself he said,

"It will have run away by the time I come out, but it will not matter too much. I can walk home, and the doctor has his own horse."

Jacob was not at all happy about waking the doctor up in the middle of the night, but it had to be done. He lifted up the big, iron knocker. It was shaped like the head of a fox. It crashed down on the door. Its echoes thundered through the house. Before its sound had died away, an upstairs window opened.

"Who is it?" asked the doctor, looking out. He had a short, rough beard and his hair was tangled with sleep.

"It's me – Jacob," was the reply. "I'm sorry indeed to wake you, doctor, but our baby is very ill. She's coughing and crying, and gasping for breath."

"Right Jacob," said the doctor briskly. "You start back home. I'll saddle my horse and be on my way as fast as I can."

"Thank you doctor. You know the house?"

"Yes, I know."

Jacob went to the side of the house. It was too much to hope that the horse would still be there, but there it was. It stood patiently, holding its head proudly. It gave a snort of greeting, and its breath formed little misty clouds in the cold air.

In a few moments Jacob was on its back again, galloping along the highroad. The lantern swung wildly, and sent leaping patterns of light over the hedges. The horse galloped on and on like the wind. Hedges, trees, and lonely cottages seemed to speed by. A duck on a wayside pond awoke and gave a small quack of surprise. A startled owl flew like a white ghost across the road. The horse's hooves rang and echoed along the highway.

Then came the turning into the muddy lane that led to Jacob's cottage. The horse slowed down to a trot, splashing through the puddles, sending mud and water flying.

"Whoa, whoa!" cried Jacob at his cottage, and the horse stopped.

"No sign of the doctor yet," thought Jacob to himself. "I'll just have time to tie you up before he comes. Then in the morning I'll do all I can to find out who your owner is."

He led the horse to the back of the cottage and tied him to an old apple tree. The moon came out from behind the clouds. It shone down on his white coat and his fine, proud head.

"You're a wonderful horse," whispered Jacob. "You couldn't have come at a better time. I'll never forget you."

Now the doctor was coming up the lane on his brown horse. He looked amazed as Jacob came round to the front gate.

"I thought you were on foot," he said. "Did you have wings?" Jacob laughed.

"You go in, Doctor," he said. "The door's not locked. I'll hold your horse till you come out."

The doctor jumped down, and put the rein into Jacob's hand. Then he said in a puzzled way,

"That's strange. The moon's out full now, and yet I can't see the white horse on the hill. I've never known that to happen before. Look. You'd think there was nothing there except smooth grass." He went up to the front door and into the house, leaving Jacob staring at the hill in front of him.

Jacob could hardly believe his eyes. The doctor was right. The moon was shining so brightly that the whole hillside was bathed in light. It was almost as light as

day, but the white horse was not there. It had gone.

"It's tied to my apple tree," thought Jacob, and he trembled a little because the whole idea was so strange. He was full of thankfulness too, because in a very short while the doctor came out of the house and said,

"Nothing to worry about now. I've given the baby some medicine. She is very ill, but I think we've caught the trouble just in time. Your wife knows what to do. I'll call again in the morning."

"Thank you Doctor. Goodnight."

"Goodnight Jacob."

The doctor hurried away on his brown horse. Jacob stared again at the bare hillside.

"I'll give the horse a drink before I go indoors," he thought and he went round to the back again. There was the apple tree, holding out its twisted branches in the moonlight. The rope was still tied to its trunk, but the white horse had slipped its head out and gone. It was nowhere to be seen.

A little later, Jacob was ready for bed. He and his wife had drunk mugs of hot cocoa. The baby had stopped crying and stopped coughing. It was breathing more easily. It had fallen asleep.

"Such a strange thing happened," said Jacob, and he started telling his wife about the white horse.

"It must have strayed from one of the farms," said his wife. "I wondered how you got to the doctor and back again so soon. But who is there with a white horse in these parts? I can't think of anyone, can you?"

"You don't understand," went on Jacob. "It was the white horse from the hill. You see – it's not there now." His wife opened the window and looked out.

"What's that then?" she asked. And there was the horse carved out of the green hillside as it always had been. There it was, white and gleaming in the moonlight.

.   .   .   .   .   .

A few days later, people in the village began talking about the white horse on the hill.

"It wants cleaning up," they said. "Its legs and its body look dirty, as if it has been splashing through mud. The grass edging needs to be cut back a bit. The chalk needs raking."

"We'll do it on Saturday," they said. "We'll get as many people as possible to help."

So on Saturday Jacob joined a crowd of people on the hillside. They worked on the horse with tools from their farms and gardens. They cut back the grass edges. They dug out weeds from the chalk. They scraped off mud and earth. They made the horse smooth and white. Then they stood back and looked proudly at their work.

"It's a fine horse," said someone.

"It's a wonderful horse," said Jacob, but only he knew *how* wonderful.

A Page of Riddles

Q. What flies and wobbles?
A. A jellycopter.

Q. What does the word "minimum" mean?
A. A very small mother.

Q. Who fries the fish in a monastery?
A. The Friar.

Q. Who cooks the chips in a monastery?
A. The chip monk.

Q. What lies on the floor of the sea and shivers?
A. A nervous wreck.

Q. Why didn't the skeleton go to the dance?
A. Because he had no body to go with.

Q. What kind of lighting did Noah have in the ark?
A. Flood lighting.

The Lady of Stavoren

Long ago, in the harbour of Stavoren, in Holland, there lived a rich widow. She had a large and beautiful house, hung with curtains of silk and velvet. She had valuable furniture and rugs, and she ate her meals from dishes of silver. She had statues of bronze and ornaments of gold. She had vases of priceless china and boxes overflowing with precious jewels.

She owned a whole fleet of ships, which she sent out to trade with different countries. She was the richest person in Stavoren, and she ruled the place as if she owned it.

Stavoren in those days was a fine city, and the chief port in that part of Holland. There were many handsome buildings and big houses lining the streets. There were many great ships coming and going in the harbour. There were many merchants and sea captains who were almost as rich as the Lady of Stavoren herself.

She did not like to think that anyone else had things as precious as her own. There was nothing – nothing at all – that she needed, but she felt that she must get something new and grand that no one else would have. It must be something special, something more valuable than anything else in the city. She wondered what the greatest treasure in the world would be. Whatever it was, she wanted to have it!

So she sent for the captain of one of her ships, and she handed him a large bag of gold.

"I want you to call at all the ports on the Baltic Sea," she said, "and I want you to buy me the greatest treasure in the world."

"What *is* the greatest treasure in the world, my Lady?" asked the captain.

"That is for you to find out," said the Lady of Stavoren.

So the captain set sail, and he called at all the ports on the Baltic Sea.

"Show me your treasures," he said at each one, "so that I may buy something for the Lady of Stavoren."

People showed him objects of silver and gold, worked by the finest craftsmen. They showed him paintings and statues by gifted artists. They showed him jewellery made by the cleverest jewellers. He looked at each thing in turn and said,

"That is very beautiful, but my Lady already has one of those," or,

"That is very valuable I am sure, but it is not so valuable as the one my Lady already has."

Soon the captain came to the last of the ports, and still he had not bought anything to take back with him.

"What *is* the greatest treasure in the world?" he asked a little group of people in the harbour.

"Gold, I suppose," replied a man.

"Or precious stones," suggested a woman.

Then an old man spoke.

"I should say wheat," he said. "We plant it and it grows. It gives us our daily bread. We could not live without it."

"Yes, wheat," agreed the woman. "It's far more valuable to us than gold or silver or precious stones."

"I believe you're right," said the captain. It was a clever answer to his question, and he thought the Lady of Stavoren might think it was the right answer too.

So the captain and his crew loaded the ship with wheat. They loaded tonnes and tonnes of it. They filled the hold with the golden grains until it could take no more. Then they set the sails and made their way back to Holland, back to the port of Stavoren.

News came to the Lady of Stavoren that her ship was on its way home, so she went down to the harbour to meet it. What had the captain brought for her, she wondered. The greatest treasure in the world – what would it be?

She stood at the harbour edge and waited while the ship was anchored. The captain came down the gang plank to greet her.

"Well, what have you brought for me?" she demanded.

"My Lady," he answered, "I have brought you a great load of wheat. Surely it is the greatest treasure in the world. We plant it and it grows. It gives us our daily bread. We could not live without it."

"You have brought what?" cried the Lady of Stavoren.

"Wheat, my Lady."

"Wheat," she almost screamed. "I asked you to bring me the greatest treasure in the world, and you have brought me wheat that any peasant can grow in his field."

The captain started to explain that wheat was far more valuable than gold or silver or precious jewels, but she would not listen.

"You can take it out of the harbour and tip it all into the sea," she shouted.

There were a lot of people standing by, listening and watching. Some of them muttered about the terrible waste. Then an old man spoke up bravely.

"Madam," he said, "why don't you give the wheat to the poor?" The Lady of Stavoren took no notice.

"Tip it all into the sea," she repeated to the captain, "and do not sail in any of my ships again."

The captain carried out her orders. He took the ship to the harbour entrance, and he and his crew tipped the wheat into the water. There were tonnes and tonnes of it. The shining, golden grains gleamed for a moment in the sunshine, and then disappeared for ever into the grey sea.

"You may be hungry yourself some day!" shouted the old man angrily to the Lady of Stavoren. She swung round sharply and walked away from the harbour.

"Hungry!" she thought. "As if I shall ever be hungry!"

But that night, a strange and violent storm arose. Waves beat wildly against the shores of Holland. Winds tore fiercely at the ports along the Baltic coast. Rain poured in torrents on the open sea. Wherever they were, the Lady of Stavoren's ships were wrecked. Every one of them was battered and broken. The whole of her fleet was lost.

And that was not all. For a while, life seemed to go on as usual in the city. Then it was found that some ships from other lands could not sail into the harbour. The waves were washing piles of sand up against the great load of wheat. The shipping channel was growing more and more narrow. The harbour was silting up. Sometimes, at low tide, the men of Stavoren tried to dig the channel free again, but at the next tide, the sand and wheat would surge forward once more, blocking the harbour.

The harbour grew narrower and narrower until entrance to the harbour was almost impossible. Ships found other ports to use. They no longer came to Stavoren. Stavoren, as a port, was dead. Merchants and sailors had to move elsewhere to make a living. Their rich houses became shabby and fell into ruins. The wealth and the trading ended. Stavoren became a small, dull little town.

"Don't even bother to visit it," say the guide books of today.

Adapted

The Fisherman's Catch

In the year 1704, a Frenchman wrote a book called *The Thousand and One Nights.* In it were many strange stories. They had come from Persia and India and Arabia and perhaps other Eastern countries too. They had been told for hundreds and hundreds of years.

Some of them were about the adventures of Sinbad the Sailor. Some were about Ali Baba and the Forty Thieves. Some were about Aladdin and the Wonderful Lamp.

The French book was translated into many other languages. Sometimes it was called *The Thousand and One Nights*, and sometimes it was called *Arabian Nights*. The stories were read and told and written over and over again in many different countries, and they are still told today. Here is one of them.

. . . . . .

Once upon a time there was a poor fisherman who lived near the sea shore with his wife and children. Every day he cast his fishing net four times into the sea. Every day he hoped to have a good catch, but whether the catch were good or bad, he never cast out his net more than four times.

One day he went down to the shore at noon and he cast his net far into the water. He waited a little while. Then he pulled at the cords, and he felt a great weight in the net.

"I must have made a good catch," he thought, and he pulled and pulled the cords, but he could not pull the net to shore. So he tied the ends of the cords to a post on the beach, and he took off his clothes and waded into the water. He swam out to the net and he pulled and pushed it, until at last he had dragged it halfway up the beach. Only then did he look to see what he had caught. It was a dead donkey!

"Ugh!" he muttered in disgust.

He pulled the net free. He wrung it out and cast it into the sea for the second time. He waited a little while. Then he pulled at the cords, and again he felt a great weight in the net.

"I must have made a good catch this time," he thought, and he pulled and pulled the cords, but he could not pull the net to shore. So, again he tied the ends of the cords to a post on the beach, and again he took off his clothes and waded into the water.

He swam out to the net and he pulled and pushed it until at last he had dragged it halfway up the beach. Only then did he look to see what he had caught. It was a huge, cracked clay pot filled with wet sand.

He pulled the net free. He wrung it out and cast it into the sea for the third time. He waited a little while until once more he felt the net grow heavy. But again, when he dragged it to the shore, he found it was full of broken pots and tangled weeds and rubbish.

"Oh Allah!" he cried. "You know I never cast out my net more than four times. Surely I shall catch some fish the fourth time!"

Then, for the fourth and last time, he cast his net out into the sea. Then for the fourth and last time, he pulled it back to the shore. What was in it this time? It was a bottle made of brass or copper. The fisherman pulled it out of the net and looked at it. It had a narrow neck which was tightly closed with lead. It bore the seal of Solomon.

"I will sell this in the market," thought the fisherman. "I ought to get about ten pieces of gold for it." The bottle felt quite heavy, and he wondered what was in it.

"I'll break the seal and look," he said to himself. He poked at the seal with his knife, and in a few moments he was able to pull the lead stopper out. He tipped the bottle a little to the side. Then he dropped it in surprise, for out poured a cloud of smoke.

It grew bigger and bigger, spreading out along the shore, and reaching up towards the sky. The fisherman stared in amazement, and, as he watched, he saw the smoke taking the shape of a huge jinnee. The jinnee was so big that his head touched the clouds though his feet were on the sand. His legs were as long as the masts of a ship, and his head was like a dome. He had a mouth

like a great cave, and teeth like rocks. His eyes blazed like burning fires, and struck terror into the fisherman.

"Oh fisherman," roared the jinnee, "I am about to kill you."

"Why? What have I done to deserve death? Have I not set you free from the bottle that was your prison?"

"All the same, I must kill you," said the jinnee, "as you will understand when I tell you my story."

"Then tell me quickly," begged the trembling fisherman. So the jinnee began,

"I sinned against the great King Solomon, so he had me imprisoned in the bottle and thrown into the depths of the sea. 'I will give great riches to the man who sets me free,' I thought to myself. But the years passed and the years passed, and no one set me free. A hundred years passed, and still no one set me free.

Then I thought, 'I will give the greatest treasures of the earth to the man who sets me free.' But the years passed and the years passed and still no one set me free. Two hundred years passed, and no one set me free. Then I grew angry and I said to myself, 'If anyone sets me free now, I will kill him.' Eighteen hundred years passed in all, and now you, fisherman, have broken open the seal of the bottle and freed me. That is why I must kill you."

"Allah, save me!" muttered the fisherman. Then he said to the jinnee, "It was good of me to set you free. You should not return good with evil."

"That cannot be helped," replied the jinnee. "You must die."

Now the fisherman knew that he was weak and the jinnee was strong. He knew the jinnee could work magic and he could not, but he thought,

"Perhaps if I use a little cunning, I can overcome him." So he said,

"Oh jinnee, before you kill me, just answer one question for me. Answer it truthfully, in the name of Solomon the Great."

When the jinnee heard the name of Solomon, he trembled and replied,

"Very well. Ask your question."

"You are so big," said the fisherman. "This bottle is not large enough to hold even your hand or your foot. How then, could your whole body have been inside it?"

"Don't you believe that I was in it?" asked the jinnee.

"No, I don't," replied the fisherman. "I will never believe it unless I actually see you get back into it."

"Watch then!" cried the jinnee, and he turned back into a cloud of smoke before the fisherman's eyes. The smoke spread along the shore and reached up towards the sky. Then gradually, it poured back into the bottle. Little by little, it twisted itself down the narrow neck until it was all inside.

At once the fisherman picked up the lead stopper and pushed it into the opening. The bottle was tightly closed again, and the wicked jinnee was safe inside.

"Now," shouted the fisherman in triumph, "I shall throw you back into the sea, and I shall warn all fishermen not to cast their nets near this part of the shore."

Then the jinnee began to beg humbly for freedom again.

"Let me out. I beg you to let me out. For the love of Allah, be merciful to me and set me free."

"Indeed I will not," said the fisherman, and he swung the bottle in his hand.

"For the love of Allah," repeated the jinnee, "let me out, and I will show you a treasure that will bring you riches till the end of your life."

At last the fisherman began to take notice of the jinnee's prayers. He made him promise that he would not harm him. He made him swear by Allah and Solomon and all the prophets.

"I swear," agreed the jinnee. Then the fisherman took the lead stopper out of the bottle, but he trembled as he did so.

Out poured the cloud of smoke as before. It grew bigger and bigger, spreading out along the shore, and reaching up towards the sky. Then it took the shape of the jinnee with his head in the clouds and his feet on the sand.

The first thing the jinnee did was to kick the bottle into the sea. This action filled the fisherman with fear again, but he said quickly,

"Remember your promise, oh jinnee! Remember that

you swore by Allah and Solomon and all the prophets."

"I remember," replied the jinnee, and he gave a loud laugh. "Follow me," he added.

Still trembling, the fisherman followed him, carrying his net.

The jinnee led the way inland, past the city and over a mountain, and down the other side. The fisherman followed, full of fear and distrust. At last they came to a wide valley, dry and bare. In the middle of it was a lake, and there the jinnee stopped. The fisherman looked into the water and saw many strange and beautiful fish. Some were red. Some were white. Some were blue, and some were yellow.

"Cast your net," said the jinnee.

The fisherman cast his net into the lake. A little later, he pulled it back to shore and he found that he had caught four fish. One was red. One was white. One was blue, and one was yellow.

"Take these fish to the king," said the jinnee, "and he will reward you. You may come and fish here every day, but only once each day." Then the jinnee stamped hard upon the ground, and at once the earth opened and swallowed him.

The fisherman hurried home and put the four fish into a bowl of water. Then, carrying the bowl upon his

head, he took it to the king's palace. The king was amazed and pleased, for never had he seen such beautiful and unusual fish as these. He ordered his servant to give the fisherman four hundred pieces of gold. This was more money than the fisherman had ever seen in his life.

He bought all sorts of food in the market, and he went home to have a good supper with his wife and children. And that, of course, was only the first of many good meals.

Adapted

45

The Deserted Station

There are nettles on the platform;
And little oaks and pines
Are growing up among the weeds
Between the railway lines;
And in the ticket office,
Where tickets used to be,
A little mouse has made its nest
And raised a family.

There are birds' nests in the rafters
And foxgloves at the door;
And dandelions and thistle plants
Are pushing through the floor.
There are brambles at the windows
And cobwebs in the grate,
And rabbits in the waiting room
Where people used to wait.

Clap Hands, Joanne

This is a true story.

Joanne was three years old. She was a pretty little girl with fair hair that tried to curl, and did not quite manage it. She had a big sister and two big brothers. She went to a nursery class in a school near by, and she had lots of friends. She was a busy, happy child, and you might have thought that she had everything she needed in life, but she had one great wish.

"I wish," she sometimes said, "I wish I had two proper hands." For Joanne had been born with only one. Her right arm stopped just below the elbow. She had a false hand and a forearm. She always wore long sleeves, so that at first glance she looked like other children, but the false hand was of very little use, and she could not do much with it at all.

She was quite clever with her left hand, but there were certain things she simply could not do with only one hand. She could not hold on safely to the ropes of a swing. She could not guide a toy tricycle. She could not thread beads. She could not hold paper still, when she was trying to use scissors. Even eating a meal was not always easy.

47

One evening, Joanne's mother was watching television when she saw something that excited her very much. She saw a little Swedish girl the same age as Joanne. Like Joanne, she had only one hand, but that was where the great difference came. The little Swedish girl had a false forearm and a false hand she could really use. She could open and close the fingers. She could pick things up. She could hold them.

Joanne's mother watched and listened. She heard that a Swedish doctor had invented the hand, and had strapped it to the little girl's arm. The hand was worked by electrodes which picked up signals from the brain.

Joanne's mother hardly dared to breathe in case she missed any important information, but the programme

48

was very short, and when it ended, she was longing to know more about it.

What was the doctor's name?

Where did he live?

How much did the false hand cost?

If it worked for the little Swedish girl, surely it might work for Joanne!

All the movements we make with our bodies are made in answer to messages from our brains. The brain sends its messages very quickly. It might say,

"Stretch out your hand. Open your fingers. Pick up the ball. Close your fingers round it." We obey the orders in a second.

The little Swedish girl's arm stopped just below the elbow, as Joanne's did. She had electrodes placed on the stump of her arm. These picked up the brain's messages and the muscle impulses, and sent them down to her hand. The hand had a small motor inside. This made the fingers open and close when the messages reached them.

The doctor on television said,

"Pick up your doll." The little girl's brain sent the message down through the nerves of the arm and on to the electrodes. The electrodes sent the message down to her plastic fingers, just as if they were on a real hand.

"Stretch out your hand," said the brain. "Open your fingers. Pick up the doll. Close your fingers over it." Her new hand obeyed the orders in a second.

Joanne's mother, of course, was not the only person in the town who had seen the programme. Other people had seen it too, and next morning lots of them were talking about it.

"Did you see the programme about the little Swedish girl with a false hand?"

"It worked like a real one, didn't it?"

"Little Joanne ought to have one like that."

"Why can't Joanne have one?"

Why? There were a number of reasons.

The doctor lived in Sweden.

It was a long way.

The hand would cost a great deal of money. Someone said it would cost a thousand pounds. Someone else said,

"No. It's two thousand. Then there's the air fare to Sweden, and the cost of staying there for a while."

"It would cost at least three thousand pounds altogether," the people decided.

Three thousand pounds! Where could Joanne's mother and father get all that money?

The answer came very soon. The parents and

teachers of Joanne's school held a meeting.

"We will collect the money," they said. "We will ask all the people in the town to help."

The part of London where Joanne lived was called Finsbury, and next to it was Islington. Suddenly it seemed as if everyone in Finsbury and Islington were trying to make money for Joanne.

Grown-ups arranged football matches, darts matches and dances. All the entrance charges went to the Joanne fund. They held raffles, and collected things to sell at auction sales. They put money boxes in shops. Old people helped. Young people helped. Schoolchildren helped. Some of them did long, sponsored walks, and others did long, sponsored swims.

"We must get three thousand pounds," everyone said.

The hand would cost a thousand pounds, but it would sometimes have to be repaired, so Joanne would need two. The journey to Sweden, and the expenses there, would take another thousand. Three thousand pounds was the target!

All through March and April, the fund grew and grew. The local paper told the story on its front page, and printed a large photograph of Joanne and her mother. A surprise gift of a hundred and fifty pounds

came from a club in the town. The Arsenal Football Team gave five hundred pounds.

The fund soon passed a thousand pounds. Then it reached two thousand, three thousand, and even more. Joanne's mother and father could hardly believe that so much money could be collected so quickly. It was wonderful to discover how many kind people there were in Finsbury and Islington.

It was now May, and there was more than enough money. Then the great day came. Joanne and her mother set out for the airport, with a crowd of people to wave them off and wish them good luck and success.

In a few hours, they were settled comfortably in a hotel in Sweden. They were to stay for two weeks. This made a very nice holiday for Joanne's mother. Two weeks without any housework or cooking to do!

Every day, she had to take Joanne to a clinic in the city. The doctor and the nurses were all very kind and helpful. The hand and the forearm were soon made. They were fitted on to Joanne, over the stump of her forearm. She did not even have to wear straps round her chest. She was quiet and patient and good, and did not really understand everything that was happening.

Then the doctor said,

"Open your new hand, Joanne. Stretch your fingers. Now curl them up. Open them again. Close them." Joanne's brain sent the messages down the nerves and muscles of her arm. The electrodes sent them onwards to the motor in her plastic hand.

Joanne opened her new hand. She stretched her new fingers. She curled them up again. She opened them. She closed them. Pleased, and a little puzzled, she glanced across at her mother and smiled. Her mother felt too full of hope and happiness to speak.

Each day at the clinic, Joanne did new things. With the doctor's help, she taught her brain to send messages down to the electrodes on her arm. These picked up the signals and sent them down to the motor in her hand.

"Open your fingers, Joanne," the doctor would say. "See if you can pick up the ball. Close your fingers round it. Hold it tightly. Now pass it to your other hand. Now pass it back to your new hand. That's right. Good girl!"

Another day he would say,

"I want you to build a tower with these bricks. No, not with your left hand. Do it with your right. Put one brick on top of another. Good girl! Now another brick, and another, and another. Clever girl! Clap hands, Joanne."

Day by day, Joanne learned to use the hand more and more, not only at the clinic, but all through the day. Soon she found that she could pick flowers, or hold an ice cream. She could even pick up beads and thread them, and make a necklace for herself. Life was very exciting!

When the two weeks ended, Joanne and her mother flew back to England. Father was at the airport to meet them.

"Daddy!" cried Joanne, and she put both her arms round his neck and gave him the first real, two-handed hug she had ever managed to do.

Everyone in Finsbury and Islington wanted to see her. People in the street, children in the school, just could not help staring at her. They had all helped to pay for the hand. Now they wanted to see it. Some of her smaller friends were a little bit disappointed. They saw Joanne picking flowers in her garden. They saw her riding a tricycle. They saw her swinging gently on her swing, holding the ropes with both hands. She looked just the same as any other little girl!

. . . . . .

The story had a very happy ending. Joanne managed so well with her new hand, that her mother wanted other children to have them too. So she wrote to all the London members of Parliament asking if the government would supply them to children in Britain who needed them.

The government acted with surprising speed. They sent doctors to Sweden to learn how to make and fit the hands. Then they chose ten little children aged three and four to try them.

"If the hands work well with these children," they said, "we will offer them, free of charge, to others."

The people of Finsbury and Islington had wanted to help one little girl, but they found that they had unexpectedly helped a great many more.

Acknowledgement for some of the facts in this story is made to the Editor of the Islington Gazette.

Harvest Mouse

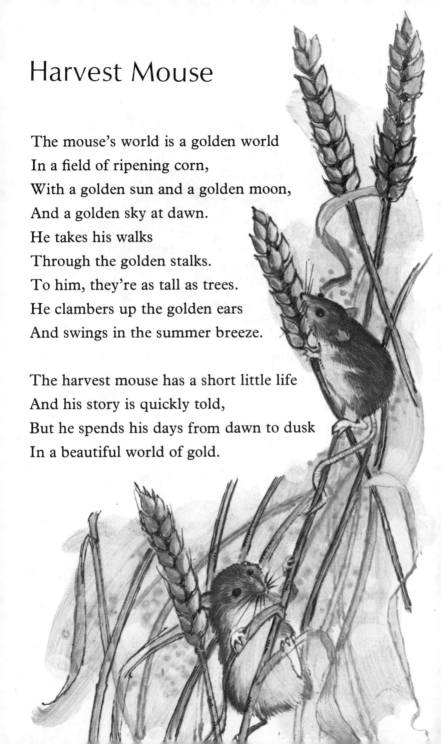

The mouse's world is a golden world
In a field of ripening corn,
With a golden sun and a golden moon,
And a golden sky at dawn.
He takes his walks
Through the golden stalks.
To him, they're as tall as trees.
He clambers up the golden ears
And swings in the summer breeze.

The harvest mouse has a short little life
And his story is quickly told,
But he spends his days from dawn to dusk
In a beautiful world of gold.

The Pony and the Yak

There seemed to be something wrong with the little pack pony. It stopped. It lay down. It would not move. Then it rose to its feet and struggled on a little way. Then it stopped again and lay down and rolled on its side as if it were going to die.

"It must be ill," murmured Dolkar, stroking it.

"It may be just that it's getting old," said Kalsang, her mother.

"And it's never been on such a long, hard journey before," added Aunt Pemba.

"Poor little pony," said Diki sadly. "It has such a lot to carry too, and not really enough food to eat."

It was true. The pony was laden with all sorts of bags and bundles. It had been growing weaker and thinner day by day, and it was often hungry, sometimes starving.

"It's a good thing the yak is still all right," remarked Dolkar.

The yak was different. It was sturdy and strong, and it was able to carry an even heavier load than the pony, as well as carrying little brother Lobsang most of the time too.

The families were making a long, long journey over the mountains to India. It was several weeks since they had left their homes in Tibet, and it would probably be many more weeks before they reached India. Dolkar was about ten or eleven at that time, and her little brother Lobsang was three. Diki, her cousin, was a gay, lively little girl of seven.

There was fighting going on in Tibet, and it had seemed safer for the two mothers and the children to leave. People also said that His Holiness, the Dalai Lama, had gone across the mountains to India. He was their god-king, and many families had decided to follow him.

The children had lost all count of time. The days and weeks were quite muddled up in their minds. Every day, every week was so difficult. Every day, every week, Dolkar, Diki and Lobsang were cold and hungry and weary; and now there was the added worry of the pony. It had to be pulled and pushed and petted, so that it was really not much help at all.

"It will die soon," said Aunt Pemba to Kalsang, when the children were out of hearing.

"Yes." They had both seen sad little piles of bones in the mountains many times. They were the bones of other ponies and yaks that had died on the journey.

"Diki will be so upset," went on Pemba. "She has always called it *her* pony."

"What can we do with it? We can't just leave it by the wayside all alone."

"We ought to reach a village this evening. We could try to sell it," suggested Pemba.

"If anyone will buy it."

"We might have to give it away if we can find anyone who will let it end its days in peace."

The little group plodded on – the mothers, the children, the yak; even, in little bursts of energy, the pony. Lobsang was wrapped in a rug and tied firmly on the yak. Diki had often ridden the pony in the past, and now she looked at it with longing. She was *so* tired.

"I should like to ride for a while," she said.

"I think the pony is too weak and tired to carry you any more, Diki."

"Yes. It's not at all well, is it?" She hugged and stroked the pony, and murmured, "My poor little pony," again and again. This seemed a good chance for Pemba to make the suggestion of selling it in the next village. To her relief, Diki shed no tears. She only said sadly, "Yes. We'd better do that."

It was a terrible day. The way was hard, and the pony lay down again and again. Many times the two mothers thought they would have to leave it. Then it would struggle to its feet once more and struggle on bravely.

The track led down and down below the snow line to a green valley, bright with spring flowers. Then in the distance it wound up again towards the next mountain pass and the glistening snow.

There was a river to cross later in the day. It was a wild, rushing river, tossing and churning through rocks and boulders. Over it was a fragile-looking bridge, made of rope and wood. It had a narrow wooden footway and nothing at the sides at all, except ropes to serve as handrails. It swung high above the water, swaying and trembling, even though no one was using it. Dolkar stared at it in horror.

"I shall never be able to cross it," she muttered.

"Yes, you will," said Kalsang quickly. "It's no worse than some of the others we've crossed."

"Oh, it is. It is."

Kalsang knew she was right, of course. It *was* worse. The families had already crossed some of these swaying bridges, but this one really was the worst yet.

"We'll never get the animals across," said Kalsang to Pemba. "They are sure-footed, I know, but this will be too much. We'll have to unload them and let them swim across."

"Yes, and I'll make two or three journeys, to take the extra luggage," agreed Pemba, adding in a whisper, "The pony cannot hope to survive."

It took quite a little planning. First the yak and the pony had to be unloaded. Pemba carried as much as she could, tied on her back. Then she and Diki crossed the

bridge. Diki was very brave and steady. She walked like a tight-rope walker, with her arms reaching up to the hand-ropes, and her head held high. The bridge swayed and shook, swayed and shook. Dolkar covered her eyes and dared not watch.

"Dolkar," said Kalsang a little later, "help me drive the animals into the water."

Both the yak and the pony were very unwilling to get wet, but at last they splashed in, and gallantly began to swim.

Everyone watched them. The water was deep and wild, and the current was strong. Pemba and Diki waited to guide them on to the rocky track on the other side. Kalsang, Dolkar and Lobsang gazed fearfully as the animals fought against the onrush of water. They were sure that the strong, tough yak would get across, but no one expected the pony to manage it.

Both animals struggled against the current. Both fought with all their strength and courage. Poor, weak little pony! This would be the end of it.

Then the unexpected happened. The yak was suddenly swept from its course, and hurled, splashing and helpless downstream. Down, down it went, as powerless as a log in the water. It was carried further and further away, becoming smaller and smaller in the distance, and then disappearing from sight. Meanwhile, by a miracle, the pony stepped ashore on the other side, and shook its shaggy coat.

"My yak! My yak!" screamed Lobsang.

"He'll be drowned!" wailed Dolkar. They wanted to run along beside the river and try to save him, but Kalsang knew it would be useless. She knew he would be dashed to pieces on the rocks, but she said,

"Perhaps someone will help him ashore a long way further down, and feed him and look after him."

Lobsang was crying, and Dolkar was in that silent state of unhappiness that Kalsang was beginning to know so well. There was no time to grieve. Pemba was already coming back along the bridge to load herself up again like a packhorse.

"If only it had been the pony," she said wistfully to Kalsang.

"I don't know what we shall do now," said Kalsang, "with the yak's load to carry as well. Oh, our good, strong yak!"

Lobsang was crying loudly, and had now changed his lament of, "I want my yak," to "I want to go home. I want to go home." Kalsang looked sadly at Pemba. She had to calm Lobsang down before she carried him on her back across the shaky, swaying bridge.

"Look, Lobsang," said Pemba. "See where Diki is standing with the pony on the other side. See where the track goes up the rocks?" He stopped crying for a moment and listened.

"Well, if you look," went on Pemba, "you'll see that the track follows the river for quite a long way, so we shall be able to look for the yak as we go." She felt it was cruel to raise his hopes, but she had to make it as easy as possible for Kalsang. Lobsang calmed down a little, and let his aunt fasten him to his mother's back with a rug woven of yak wool. Dolkar had her usual struggle with her fears.

"Shall I crawl on my hands and knees with my eyes shut, or shall I try to walk upright and look ahead, as Diki always does?" she wondered. She decided on the second way. She would go very slowly, clinging to the ropes at each side. She stepped on to the bridge. It swayed and shook, swayed and shook. Dolkar's heart thumped in terror. She stood still.

"Go on, Dolkar," said Kalsang, coming just behind her, with Lobsang and a pack of blankets on her back. Dolkar took a deep breath, and gazed ahead at Pemba and Diki and the pony. She put one foot carefully before the other, and began to cross.

Soon they were all safely over, with the bags and bundles stacked on the rocks beside them. They did not dare to add anything to the pony's usual load, so there was all the yak's luggage to share between them. Dolkar and Diki helped by tucking a few small things

inside their chubas (the cross-over garment that most Tibetans wore). They also took a rug each, and wore it like a cloak. Pemba and Kalsang carried blankets and food, animal fodder and skin bottles of water, and dried yak dung for the camp fires.

"You have too much there, Pemba," said Kalsang. "Let me take some more."

"No. You have Lobsang to carry," replied Pemba.

"But it's too much for you. Let's go through it all again, and see what we can leave behind."

"I'll manage," said Pemba bravely. "I'll try for a while anyway."

The track went along beside the river for some distance. The yak, of course, was nowhere to be seen. The pony, meanwhile, seemed to have found new strength.

"You'd think the icy water would have killed it," remarked Pemba, "but it really seems to have made it feel better."

"Dear little pony," murmured Diki. "I don't think it's going to die after all."

By evening of course, they were nowhere near the village they had hoped to reach. They were stumbling and scrambling up the mountain-side, far from anywhere. They were lucky to find a tumbledown hut for shelter. It belonged to a wandering herdsman, who used it only now and again.

"This will be better than sleeping in the open," they thought. They spread out the rugs inside the hut. They put down their bundles, and built a cheerful little fire of yak dung outside the door. Kalsang unpacked some food – yak cheese and rice cakes. Pemba put the pot on to boil for tea. The dry yak dung glowed and sent out little spurting flames. The smell of smoke and earthiness was wafted away on the still air. Darkness dropped down like a curtain, and the sky was lit with stars.

There was a sudden noise that made mothers and children jump. Someone or something was coming near. What was it? Who was it? There was a shuffling sound and an old familiar snort.

"My yak! My yak!" cried Lobsang, and his voice was shrill with joy.

There it stood – Lobsang's yak – bruised and battered, and cut in places by the rocks, but tough and hardy, and ready to give uncomplaining service once again.

The Coopers' Dance

This is a true story about the city of Munich in Germany.

It was the year 1464. The city was very quiet. There were no carts rumbling along over the cobbles. There were no women chatting in the doorways. There were no children playing in the squares. Windows and shutters were closed. The streets were deserted, and sadness hung over them like a black cloud.

Old people and young people were ill. Rich and poor were dying. The plague strode through the city, striking first at one house, then at another. In one house it might kill a single child. In the next it might attack a whole family. The houses were dark, and the air in the rooms was stale. Many people were getting short of food, but scarcely anyone dared go to market to buy more. The plague – when would it end? When would the people dare to go out of doors?

The first people brave enough to do it were the coopers. They were the men who made the big wooden barrels for beer, and the vats for cheese. They were the men who made the water butts and the washing tubs. Often in the spring they marched and sang through the streets and gathered in the squares and danced their spring dance.

"We won't be able to do it this year," they said.

"I think we *should* do it," said one. "I think we should do it early – this very week. The people have been sad long enough. They have shut themselves up in their dark, stuffy rooms for weeks. They need to come out of doors and breathe the fresh air again. If we dance in the streets, the healthy ones will come out and watch us."

"But the plague," said someone. "We may spread the plague even more."

"That is possible, but it is also possible that the fresh air might blow it away. Let us trust in God. Let us believe that He will help us."

So, early one morning that week, the coopers dressed in their festive clothes. They wore red jackets, black trousers and yellow leather aprons. They wore white socks, and shoes with silver buckles. They wore black handkerchiefs round their necks, and little green caps trimmed with blue and white feathers.

Some of the men carried fiddles and other stringed instruments. Some of them carried wooden hoops, decorated with greenery and bound round with gaily coloured ribbons. There were thirty men altogether.

They started playing a merry tune and went marching and singing down the street.

Shutters were pushed aside. Windows were opened. Heads appeared. People peeped out.

"The coopers are about! The coopers are about!"

"Surely no one will go out and watch them!"

At first no one did. Then slowly one person and then another dared to step into the street.

"Please Mother, may we go out?" begged children who were weary of being indoors.

Up and down marched the coopers, stopping outside the houses to dance their dance and play their tricks. The man who led the others told many jokes, and made everybody laugh. One man balanced three full glasses of wine on the inside of his hoop. He raised it up above his head. He held it low and jumped through it without spilling a drop of the wine.

"Come out! Come out!" called the coopers. "Trust in God and come out into the fresh air."

Gradually more and more people opened their doors and went out to watch the coopers. They followed them through the streets. They watched them dancing and stepping and leaping high above the ground. They watched them swinging their gaily decorated hoops. Mothers, fathers and children stood in the squares and laughed at the coopers' jokes and tricks, and for a while all their sadness and worry was forgotten. The brave coopers had brought the city to life again.

That was in the year 1464, but the coopers still dance in Munich during the week before Shrove Tuesday. They wear their festive clothes and dance their old dances every seventh year. They sing their old songs and do their old tricks. They do it in memory of the brave coopers who called the people out into the fresh air at the time of the plague.

The School-on-Wheels

Mandy and Karen Stevens were twins. They were ten years old and they lived with their mother and father and their little brother, Johnny, who was three. Their home was in a great deep forest in Canada, far, far from any town. Their father had to keep a certain section of the railway track in good repair, so the family lived in a wooden house not far from the railway line.

The children had never seen a town or village, or even a shop or a street, and the only sounds they heard were the sounds of the forest, and sometimes the whistle of an engine and rattle of wheels as a train came rolling up the track.

At the beginning of this story it was springtime. It was Sunday evening, and the children were waiting and listening for a special train – a goods train that stopped there once in every six weeks.

"It's late," said Karen in an anxious voice.

"Oh I hope it comes," wailed Mandy.

"Of course it will come," said Mother. "There! Listen." They kept quite still and listened. Yes, there it was – a faint throbbing sound in the distance, and then a far-away whistle, and then a jogging rattle, getting louder and nearer, louder and nearer.

74

Karen jumped up and down and clapped her hands, and Johnny turned head over heels on the floor.

"May we go?" asked Mandy.

"Yes. We'll all go," said Father. So Mother, Father, Mandy, Karen and Johnny hurried through the trees just in time to see the long goods train screech to a halt.

Now you might wonder what was so special about this train. One or two trains roared through the forest nearly every day. What was so exciting about *this* one?

Well, although it was a goods train, carrying such things as iron and coal and bales of wool to a distant town, it pulled along a special coach with it, which it unhooked and left in a siding, before roaring on its way.

The special coach was a school-on-wheels. It came once in six weeks, and it stayed five days. It was beautifully fitted out with a classroom, a cloakroom and a store cupboard. It had also a living room, two bedrooms and a modern kitchen and bathroom for the two teachers, and their son, Andrew.

Many children in Canada live so far from a school, that a school-on-wheels is the only way that teaching can be given to them. So, like Mandy and Karen they go to school for one week, and then have five weeks' homework to do before the train brings the school-on-wheels round again.

"There are Mr and Mrs Macdonald," said Father, as the two teachers waved from the windows.

"And there's Andrew," added Karen. "May we stay awhile and play with him?" For Andrew, school must have been very unusual indeed, for the school-on-wheels was his home, and every week he had different children to share the classroom with him, until the six-weeks' journey started all over again.

So Sunday evening passed happily, with Mother and Father hearing five weeks' news from Mr and Mrs Macdonald, and with Mandy, Karen, Johnny and Andrew playing together.

Next morning, Mandy and Karen were ready for school long before it was time to go.

"Not yet, not yet," Mother kept saying. "Mr and Mrs Macdonald won't have cleared away their breakfast things."

"I want to go to school," wailed Johnny. "I want to go with Mandy and Karen."

"When you're a big boy," said Karen.

Then at last it was time to go, and Mandy and Karen raced through the trees to the siding. Even then they were very early, but other excited children were early too, though they had made very long journeys to reach the school-on-wheels.

Some children came on horseback. Some had walked a long way through the forest. Some had paddled thirty

kilometres or more up the river in canoes. They all lived in lonely places, for their fathers were hunters, or woodcutters or farmers. In the winter they often had to come on sledges or walk on snowshoes, but none of the children ever missed school if they could possibly get there.

What a chattering there was as the children greeted each other, and met the teachers again, and brought out their bundles of five weeks' homework! Then when they had played a little and told each other their news, they settled down in the classroom and started their lessons.

The school week always passed so quickly – Monday, Tuesday, Wednesday, Thursday, Friday. Friday afternoon seemed to come in no time.

"Oh, I wish you could stay longer," said Mandy to Mrs Macdonald.

"So do I," she replied. "But other children are waiting at different places up the line, and how disappointed they would be if we didn't reach them in time!"

The different children said goodbye, and saddled their horses, or set off tramping through the forest or paddling down the river in their canoes. In twos and threes and small groups they waved and were gone, until only Mandy and Karen were left.

"May Andrew come and play with us until you're ready to go, Mrs Macdonald?" asked Karen.

"Yes, for about half an hour."

So Andrew ran home with Mandy and Karen, and played with them. Meanwhile a goods train had arrived, and the school-on-wheels was hooked up and pulled back on to the main line, ready for its next journey.

"I'd better go back," said Andrew, long before the half hour had passed. He was always afraid that his home might go without him.

"We'll walk back with you," said Karen.

"Johnny come too?" asked Johnny.

"You're soon back," said Mrs Macdonald a little later as the four children stood beside the train. "Bring them inside, Andrew. Let Johnny look round the classroom."

Up the steps clambered the children and back into the railway carriage classroom. Mandy, Karen and Andrew started doing a jigsaw puzzle together, and Johnny wandered round the room, staring up at the pictures on the walls, and looking at the books that the smaller children used. Meanwhile Mrs Macdonald was in the kitchen, putting things in the cupboards, and Mr Macdonald was outside, chatting to the engine driver.

Johnny became tired of looking at books, and he opened the door that led to the store cupboard. It was a big, light, walk-in cupboard, and he went inside and closed the door behind him. The other children were so busy with their puzzle that they did not notice what he was doing.

To Johnny the cupboard was like a treasure house.

His mother had told him about towns where there were toy shops. This surely must be a toy shop! There were games and puzzles. There were rolls of coloured paper, and boxes of crayons and tins of paint. There were all sorts of interesting things.

After a while Mrs Macdonald came to the door of the classroom and said,

"You must go now children. We're just about to start. Where's Johnny?"

"I thought he was in the kitchen with you," replied Mandy.

"No. I think he must have gone back home," added Karen.

"Andrew, just go and look in our own rooms to make sure he's not there," said Mrs Macdonald. "Mandy and Karen you jump down now."

Mandy and Karen climbed down from the train and stood well back. Andrew put his head out of his bedroom window and shouted,

"It's all right. He's not here." Mr Macdonald went into the coach and closed the door. Then he and Mrs Macdonald called out goodbye, and the school-on-wheels went on its way, slowly at first, then picking up speed and disappearing with a chug and a roar through the forest.

Mandy and Karen waved till it was out of sight. Then they walked back towards home. They usually felt rather flat and sad when the school-on-wheels went away. Their mother always said they were like two burst balloons, but she knew they would become lively and happy again very soon.

Meanwhile what about Johnny? He was so interested, exploring the store cupboard, and sometimes sitting on the floor playing with different things, that he did not even notice that the train was moving. Then when he did suddenly feel and hear the chug, chug of the coach, he still did not guess that he was being taken away. He just felt a bit tired and thought he would like to go back to his mother.

He opened the cupboard door and went into the classroom. Mandy, Karen and Andrew were not there. At the same moment, he saw trees rushing past the window. Now he did feel frightened!

Mr and Mrs Macdonald and Andrew were all standing in the kitchen talking. Suddenly they heard a small shuffle in the open doorway that led to the corridor. They looked. They stared! There was Johnny – three years old – going further and further away from his home in the forest.

"Want to go home now," he said in a small voice.

"Johnny!" exclaimed Mr Macdonald.

"But he wasn't in any of the rooms," protested Andrew. "I looked in every one."

"This is what I have always dreaded," murmured Mrs Macdonald. "Ever since we've been teaching in the school-on-wheels, I've always dreaded that some child, somewhere, would get left on the train."

"Well, now it's happened," said Mr Macdonald. "Johnny, where have you been hiding all this time?" But Johnny did not answer. His face crinkled up into tears, and he opened his mouth and yelled.

. . . . . .

By this time, of course, Mandy and Karen were getting worried too.

"Where's Johnny?" asked their mother, when they arrived home without him.

"He came home on his own," said Karen.

"I haven't seen him." said Mother.

They looked quickly through the house, but Johnny was not there.

"You should have looked after him," said Mother. "You shouldn't have let him out of your sight." Mandy and Karen felt miserable and ashamed because they knew it was true. They *shouldn't* have let him out of their sight. They had both been so busy and happy doing the jigsaw puzzle with Andrew, that really they had forgotten all about their little brother.

"He must have wandered into the forest," said Mother. "Mandy, you wait here in case he comes back.

Karen, you walk along to the siding and look for him. I'll go into the forest."

Time passed. Mandy waited, but Johnny did not come home. Karen came back, but she had not found Johnny. Mother came back, but *she* had not found Johnny. Father returned from work.

"Johnny's lost," said Mother.

"He hasn't got left in the school-on-wheels has he?" asked Father. No one had mentioned this. Perhaps they had not thought of it, or perhaps they had not dared to think of it.

"Better to be in the school than lost in the forest," said Father.

"But the school won't be back for five weeks," sobbed Mandy.

Father asked the children lots of questions. Did Johnny go into the classroom? Yes. What did he do in there? Look at books. Did they actually see him leave the classroom? No. Did they actually see him get off the train? No.

"So you just thought he must have got off and gone home," said Father.

"Andrew searched all the rooms," put in Mandy.

"And if Andrew searched the train as well as you two looked after your little brother," said Father angrily, "it's quite possible that Johnny's still there, asleep in a corner somewhere. Meanwhile we'll have to keep searching the forest."

It was an hour now since the school-on-wheels had left. Johnny could have wandered so far into the forest that he might never be found. And soon it would be dark.

"Mandy, you stay at home and wait," said Father. "Karen, you go along by the railway track to the left." At that moment a sound startled them. It was the peep-peep signal of the two-way radio. Father darted across to it and put on the headphones.

"Calling Forest Side," he heard. "Calling John Stevens at Forest Side."

"Hullo, hullo, John Stevens of Forest Side here," he replied.

Mother, Mandy and Karen stood like statues. They were almost afraid to breathe in case they should disturb Father. They hoped and hoped it might be news of Johnny, but they were very afraid that it might be only a message about a change in the time of a train, or a warning that a tree had fallen across the line somewhere. They wished they knew who was speaking, and what he was saying. Father's voice meanwhile told them little. He just said,

"Yes. Yes. Spruce Vale?" Then his face lit up and he spoke with relief and excitement; and Mother and the children knew then, that Johnny was safe somewhere. They could hardly wait for Father to say goodbye and take off the headphones.

"Johnny's in the school-on-wheels," he explained. "It was Mr Denver speaking from Spruce Vale. Mr Macdonald threw out a note to him as the train passed. The school stops at Blue Creek at ten o'clock tonight. Mr Macdonald will get the Section Foreman to radio a message to me from there."

So Johnny was safe. Mother was so relieved that she began to cry, and Mandy cried too to keep her company, but Karen could not understand why they should cry when Johnny was *safe*.

As for Johnny, he had to spend the night in the

school-on-wheels, sharing Andrew's bed, in a siding at Blue Creek. It was lucky for him that a passenger train was going through next morning and that the guard agreed to look after him, and that the driver agreed to stop at Forest Side to deliver him safely to his parents.

The passengers must have wondered why their train should stop at Forest Side. It was such a lonely place. They all hung out of the windows and saw Mother and Father and Mandy and Karen waiting in the trees. Then they saw the guard jump down and lift a little three-year-old boy off the train.

"Does he belong to you?" the guard asked Mother with a grin. But there was no need to ask, for Johnny jumped straight into her arms and put his arms round her neck and held on tightly as if he would never let go.

And away at Blue Creek a lot of lonely children were getting excited because when Monday came, *their* week would start at the school-on-wheels.

The Feather

When the wild grey geese flew over the town
A single soft feather came floating down.
Soft, soft, downy and grey,
It caught on the breeze and drifted my way.
When the wild grey geese flew over our street
A single soft feather fell at my feet.
Soft, soft, downy and grey,
It filled me with happiness all through the day.

The Testing of Thor

In olden days many nations and tribes and people believed in their own special gods. The gods sometimes behaved very badly and most of them had great powers of magic.

Thor was a god of the Norse land, which we now call Norway. He was very strong and boastful and bad-tempered, and was known as the god of thunder.

One day he set out on a journey with his servant and another god called Loki. He wanted to go to the land of the giants. He knew the giants were great, strong men, but he was quite sure he would show himself to be stronger than they were.

The three men walked all day, and when darkness fell they began to look for somewhere to spend the night. The country was lonely and wild and there seemed to be no sheltered place to sleep. Then, after a while they came to a large building. It was open at one end so they looked inside. There was nothing in it, not a bed, not a table, not a chair.

"Not very comfortable," said Thor, "but it is better than nothing, I suppose." So they went inside, lay on the floor and fell asleep.

In the middle of the night they were awakened by a terrible noise. It was a sort of snoring sound, but it was so loud that it made the whole earth tremble.

"We'd better hide in case we are attacked," said Loki. But where could they hide? They groped round in the darkness and found that there was another room leading off from the vast hall. It was a long, narrow room, so they crept into it and spent the rest of the night there. They were quite unable to sleep however, because the terrible noise went on all the time.

In the morning it was still going on – shaking the building and shaking the ground itself. As soon as it was light, Thor, Loki and the servant crept out of the building and looked round. They saw at once what was causing the noise. A huge giant was lying asleep on the ground near by, snoring and snoring with every breath he took.

Now Thor had a magic hammer which he always carried with him, and if he threw it at anything it would fly back to his hand. For a moment he thought of throwing it at the sleeping giant, but just then the giant awoke and sat up.

"Who are you?" he roared.

"I am Thor, the god of thunder," replied Thor. "And who, may I ask, are you?"

"Skrymir is my name," said the giant. "I seem to have lost one of my gloves. Have you seen it anywhere?" He looked round. Then he said,

"Ah! Here it is," and he picked up the large building that Thor and his friends had just left. It was (if you can believe it) the giant's glove. The vast hall was the hand, and the long narrow room at the side was the thumb. Thor, Loki and their servant were too amazed to do anything but stare.

"And where are you going?" asked Skrymir.

"To the land of the giants," they answered.

"I am going that way," said Skrymir, "but I can see that you are too weak and feeble to keep pace with me."

Thor was angry at this remark, but as he watched Skrymir stride off swiftly into the distance, he thought that perhaps it was true.

Soon Thor, Loki and their servant saw a great city in

the distance. The buildings were so high that their roofs were hidden in the clouds.

"This must be the land of the giants," they said. They reached the city about midday and came almost at once to a huge hall. The door was open, so they walked inside. There was a large crowd of giants in the hall, and at the end the giant king sat on a great throne.

"Who are these three travellers?" asked the king.

"I am the god of thunder," replied Thor in his usual boastful way.

"Thor the god of thunder?" repeated the king. "I am indeed surprised to see that you are such a weak-looking little creature. Now I wonder what you and your friends can do to show us your strength. If you wish to stay here awhile, you will each have to do something that none of our own people can do so well."

Then Loki spoke. He said,

"I can eat faster than anyone else. Bring forward the man who can eat as fast as I can."

"That is easy," replied the king, and he called a giant forward from the crowd. Others put a long wooden trough on the ground and filled it with food from end to end.

"We will see who eats his way to the middle first," said the king. "Ready, Go!" Munch, munch. Crunch, crunch. The contest started. In no time at all, both men had eaten their way to the middle.

"Well, your man has not beaten me," said Loki rather feebly. Then he saw that the giant had eaten half the wooden trough, as well as the food it held, so there was no doubt at all about who was the winner.

"Now," said the king. "What can your servant do?"

"I can run faster than anyone in the world," replied the servant. So a giant was called forward to run against him. The race was held on a great stretch of open land, and though Thor's servant ran like the wind, the giant raced him easily.

"Now, Thor," said the king. "What can you do?"

"I can drink more swiftly than anyone else," boasted Thor.

"Very well. We have a great drinking horn here," said the king. "Our fastest drinkers can empty it at a single gulp. Others, who are not so fast, can drink it in two gulps, and we have no one who cannot empty it in three."

Thor glanced at the great horn, filled as he thought with wine.

"I am thirsty," he said. "It will be easy for me to drain it at a single gulp." He held it to his lips and took a great gulp. He was sure he had emptied the horn, but when he looked he saw he had made hardly any difference to it at all.

He lifted it a second time and drank so deeply that again he was sure he had emptied it. But when he looked he saw that it was nearly as full as before. Then he lifted it to his lips a third time, and he drank and drank until he could drink no more.

"What a feeble effort!" said the giant king. "The horn is still almost full. You are not half so strong as you think you are."

"Let me have a fair fight with one of your men," said Thor angrily. "Then I will show you how strong I am."

The king laughed.

"I do not think any of our men would wish to fight against such a weak little creature as you," he said. "But perhaps my old nurse might like to try."

He called an old, old woman into the hall. She was so old that she had no teeth left, and her hair had long ago turned white. Thor was afraid to touch her in case he knocked her over, but to his surprise she rushed at him and fought as fiercely as a young man would do. Thor was forced to fight back with all his strength, but in a few moments the old nurse had thrown him to the ground. The hall rang with the laughter of the giants.

Thor felt ashamed and angry He wished to return home at once, but darkness was now falling, and the king invited the three men to a great feast and offered them beds for the night.

When morning came the king walked with them to the city gate, and a little way outside it.

"Did you enjoy your visit to the land of the giants?" he asked.

"Enjoy it!" said Thor angrily. "The visit brought only shame and anger to me."

"Now that you are out of our land, I will tell you that we cheated you," said the king.

"How did you cheat?"

"The giant who beat Loki in the eating contest was not really a giant. He was Fire. Fire can consume more than any man can eat.

The giant who ran against your servant was not really a giant. He was Thought. Thought can travel more swiftly than any man.

The horn from which you drank was standing in the sea. No man can drain the sea dry.

The old woman who fought with you was not really a woman. She was Old Age itself. No man can fight against Old Age and win."

As Thor listened to the giant king, he became more and more angry. He lifted his magic hammer to throw at him in fury, but in a flash the giant king disappeared, and the city with him. Thor found himself standing with Loki and their servant in a great stretch of lonely country.

He had been cheated from beginning to end, but perhaps it had done him a little good.

Adapted

Isabella

Once upon a time there was an artist who was wandering round a Spanish town looking for a picture to paint. The sun was hot and the sky was blue, and here and there among modern shops and offices, there were one or two buildings left from earlier days, old and crumbling and beautiful.

The artist walked on, looking at each one. He carried an easel and paints under his arm, and held a small, folding stool in the other hand.

Suddenly he came to an opening where a covered archway of stone led to what seemed to be a garden. The artist walked under the archway, and looked inside. Then he stood still and took a deep, deep breath. *Here* was a picture to paint!

He saw a small palace, built on four sides of a square courtyard, with shady, arched balconies along the full length of every floor. The building was old and crumbling; and clusters of geraniums tumbled from some of the archways like small, scarlet waterfalls.

The courtyard was paved with slabs of stone, and in the middle was a well with a grating on the top. Everything was quiet and still, as if the people who lived there were fast asleep. Everything was quiet and still and beautiful.

"I wonder who lives here," thought the artist. "And I wonder if he will let me paint the palace."

Then he saw a little girl. She came out of a door on the ground floor, and she stood still and stared at him. She had black hair and dark eyes. She wore a blue frock, and her feet were bare.

"Good afternoon," said the artist to her. "What is your name?"

"Isabella," she answered.

"Isabella," repeated the artist. "And are you a princess?"

"No," replied Isabella, and she giggled a little at the thought.

"But you live in a palace," said the artist, "so you must be a princess."

"No I'm not," said Isabella, and she giggled again.

Quiet and still! Did the artist think that everyone here was fast asleep? He did, but he soon knew better, for at the sound of his voice, little dark heads appeared at different places on the balconies, and little bare feet came padding out of open doors on all four sides of the courtyard.

Then the artist guessed that though the building must once have been a palace, it was now divided into flats and rooms for lots and lots of ordinary families. The days of rich dukes and beautiful princesses had gone. Now the palace belonged to all these dark little Spanish children and their mothers and fathers and relations.

"And quite right too," thought the artist.

Isabella's mother was standing beside her now, so the artist said,

"May I sit in the courtyard and paint this beautiful building?" He was English, but he spoke good Spanish.

"Yes, of course," replied Isabella's mother, rather

surprised that anyone should think the shabby old palace was still beautiful.

So the artist set up his little folding stool, and stood his easel in the courtyard. He arranged his canvas and he opened his paint box and sorted out some fat little tubes of paint, and he began his picture. Slowly the children crept nearer and nearer, staring at him curiously, and gazing at the faint dabs of colour that were the beginning of his painting.

The children were poor, and some of them were shabby, and most of them had bare feet, but this was because it was the only way to keep their toes cool. They were gay little children with lovely Spanish names, like Juanita and Pepita for the girls, and Pedro and Ferdinando and Chico for the boys. Chico was still a baby, only about two years old, but he stood with the others and stared at the artist, and he stared very hard at the fat little tubes of paint, and he wished he could play with them.

By the end of the afternoon the artist had not done very much of the picture because he was a slow and careful painter. He gathered up his things and put them under his arm, and said goodbye.

"Mañana," he added, which is Spanish for "to-morrow." "Tomorrow I will come again."

So he went the next afternoon, and the next and the next. Then he said to Isabella,

"Do you think your mother could find a little space in your rooms for my painting things, so that I do not have to carry them backwards and forwards every day?"

"I will ask her," answered Isabella, and in a moment she came back and said,

"Yes. My mother says we will be pleased to look after your painting things. She says we will stand the easel and the stool against the wall in the corner, and we will put the brushes and the box of paints on the floor under the cupboard. We will look after them and keep them safe for you."

"Thank you," said the artist. "Thank you."

So every day after that, before the artist went away, he and Isabella carried his things to Isabella's rooms. Isabella stood the easel and the stool against the wall in the corner, and she put the brushes and the box of paints on the floor under the cupboard.

"I will keep them safe for you," she said, and she felt proud and happy to be helping the artist in this way.

Soon the artist finished the picture, and started another one. For the second one, he sat beside the well in the courtyard, and faced a different way. Every afternoon he came, and every afternoon, when he went

away, he gave Isabella his painting things to keep safe for him.

Then one afternoon he did not come.

"Where is he?" asked the children.

"Mañana," said Isabella. "I expect he will come tomorrow." But he did not come the next day, nor the next, nor the next.

"Where can he be?" asked the children.

Then after a week or two, some of them began to say he would probably never come again. But Isabella kept his painting things safe for him, because she knew that he *would* come again one day to fetch them.

Now the children did not know it, but the artist had fallen ill, and a friend of his had taken him back to England by air. So the easel and the stool and the brushes and the paints stayed in Isabella's house, and the artist did not come to fetch them.

"Let *us* paint pictures with his paints," said Ferdinando and Juanita one day.

"No," said Isabella firmly. "They don't belong to us."

"Let *us* try the paints," said Pedro and Pepita one day.

"No," said Isabella firmly. "They don't belong to us." And Chico, who was still a baby, only about two years old, peeped round Isabella's open door and stared at the box where the fat little tubes of paint were kept, and he *wished* he could play with them.

Then one morning when the courtyard was quiet, Chico did a very bad thing. All the children were at school, and there was no one to play with him. His mother was busy cleaning her rooms, and Isabella's mother was away at the wash-house down the street. Isabella's door was open, for hardly any doors were ever shut.

Chico peeped round Isabella's door and stared at the box of paints on the floor under the cupboard. Then he went in and pulled it out and opened it. There were the fat little tubes of paint, lots and lots of them. Some of them were hardly used, and some of them were twisted and flat, and some of them had been squeezed almost empty.

Chico took a handful of the fattest tubes, and walked out into the courtyard with them. He walked over to the well where the artist used to sit. He leaned over, and he dropped one fat little tube through the grating into the water. Plop! It made a satisfying little noise. He dropped another fat little tube through the grating into the water. Plop! Another one. Plop! Another. Plop!

Ferdinando's mother saw Chico at the well, but she knew the grating was in place, and he could not come to any harm. Then Chico went back to Isabella's room, and he took some more of the fat little tubes. He put them on the floor a moment while he closed the box. Then he pushed the box back in its place under the cupboard so that no one would know it had been moved.

He stuffed some tubes into his pockets, and clasped others in his hot little hands. Then he walked to the well again. He leaned over and dropped one fat little tube through the grating into the water. Plop! He

dropped another one. Plop! Another! Plop! Another! Plop!

Soon he had none left in his pockets and none in his hands. He was tired of the game now, and he wandered back into his own room, and curled up on the floor and fell asleep.

"What a good little boy he is," thought his mother. "No trouble at all."

A week later, the postman brought a postcard for Isabella. This was a great event, for none of the children had ever had a letter or a postcard before. It was from the artist in England, but it was written in Spanish, and it explained that he had been ill.

"Please take care of my painting things," it said. "I will come and get them at the end of the summer."

Isabella showed the postcard to everyone, dancing from door to door with it, and feeling very proud and happy. Then she went indoors and dusted the artist's stool and his easel and his paint box. The paint box rattled as she pulled it out from under the cupboard. It rattled again as she lifted it up to dust the underside of it. Funny! It hadn't rattled before. It had been too full.

She felt puzzled and a little worried. She thought she had better look inside and see that everything was all right. She opened the box. She saw the twisted, flat tubes of paint, and those that had been squeezed almost empty. She saw two or three of the fat ones that were hardly used – but where were the rest? Where were all the other fat little tubes? There were scarcely any of them left! She had promised to look after them – and they had gone!

. . . . . .

Weeks passed by and Isabella did not find the missing tubes of paint. She asked all the children but no one knew anything about them. She even asked Chico, but he was only a baby and no one could ever get a proper answer from *him*.

Slowly the summer passed, hot, dry and always sunny. Soon it would end and then the artist would come and ask for his painting things. Isabella felt very unhappy. The artist had trusted her, and she had *promised* to keep the things safe.

The well in the courtyard dried up, as it did nearly every summer, and the mothers and children had to go down the street to fetch water from a pump. Isabella went with the others one day, carrying a large jug and half-listening to the chatter.

"Mañana," she heard Juanita say. "Tomorrow they are coming to clean out the well."

This was exciting news. Isabella remembered when the well had been cleaned out once before, and all the children had gathered round, hoping the men would find some treasure down there. The men had found only a few small coins and one or two hairclips and an old tin. Perhaps this time they *would* find treasure.

So next day she stood about in the courtyard with the other children and watched the men take the grating off the well. Like the others, she went away from time to time, to go indoors or to fetch water – and then came back to see what the men had found. Strange how some people must drop things down wells!

The men found –

a lot of muddy slime

an empty baked bean tin

a small broken sandal

two pieces of wood

three buttons

and a number of fat little tubes of paint!

Two people pounced on them – Chico and Isabella. Chico picked up one in each grubby hand. Isabella almost snatched them away from him and then put them all in an empty basket that Pedro was holding. She carried them quickly indoors and looked at them one by one.

They were unharmed. Their caps were still screwed in place. The paint inside was still safe. Only the labels had been washed away. Never mind. She could write new ones.

Carefully and slowly she wrote neat little labels and stuck them on the tubes, after first peeping inside at the colour of the paint. And while she was doing this, she suddenly remembered seeing little Chico some weeks ago with a dab of red paint on his shirt. Chico must have taken the paints and dropped them down the well!

Next afternoon, the very next afternoon, the artist came striding into the courtyard. The children rushed to greet him. They clung round him and looked so pleased to see him that his heart was filled with happiness.

"And how's my Isabella?" he asked, lifting Isabella up to see how much she had grown.

"Are my paints still safe?" he added.

"Yes," said Isabella. "Come and see."

So the artist went to Isabella's door, and Isabella

showed him his stool and his easel leaning against the wall in the corner. Then she pulled out the paint box from under the cupboard. She opened the lid. The artist looked a little surprised. When he had left the paints, they had been labelled with the strange names that paints usually have – ultramarine and burnt sienna, yellow ochre and crimson lake. Now they had ordinary plain names, very neatly written. They had names like blue and brown, yellow and black, green and red.

"Really *much* more sensible," he thought.

Goats in History

Goats have been friends of man since ancient times. They have lived beside him and given him rich milk and cheese. They have given him meat and leather and warm goatskin. Sometimes they have played quite an active part in his life; and now and again, in different countries, they have stepped into history.

1. Goats in Switzerland

Long ago, a small town on a hill in Switzerland was attacked by soldiers from another province. The people of the town fought bravely, but their numbers were much smaller than those of the enemy. Already the town castle was in flames, and the people were being pushed back inside the walls they were trying to defend. All day the battle went on.

Then evening came, and the enemy drew back into the valley to rest for the night.

"One more attack in the morning," they said, "and the town will be ours."

The sun sank low in the sky. The valley was filled with mist and the first shades of darkness.

Suddenly there was a cry of alarm, and the enemy looked up in horror. Down from the town came what seemed to be another attacking army. It was not easy to see plainly through the mist, but it seemed that a wild crowd of men came running down the hill with a great noise and clamour. The strangest and most frightening thing was that each man had a light around his head.

The enemy scattered and fled, and the town was saved. And what about the army that had come to help the people at the right moment? It was not made up of soldiers or fighting men. It was simply a crowd of goats sent out by the women of the town. Each goat had a large, clanging bell round its neck. Each goat had a candle, or a glowing torch fixed between its ears. The women had chased the whole flock towards the enemy with loud cries. So the goats had saved the town.

2. Goats in Ireland

Long ago, a band of soldiers were planning to attack a village in Ireland. They crept along the side of the mountain, hiding in the bushes. The people in the village below knew nothing of this. On the mountain-side, however, a herd of wild goats was grazing. Suddenly the goats saw swords and shields flashing in the sun and gleaming in the bushes. This frightened them and they ran wildly down into the village.

Then the village people knew that the enemy must be on the mountain-side, and they were able to attack first and drive them away.

Ever since then, a goat has been chosen every year as king of a fair that lasts three days. He is given a crown and he is trimmed with ribbons and flowers. He is set up on a small high platform decked with flags and fairy lights. People from many parts of Ireland come to the fair, and look up at the goat king.

3. Goats in Germany

Every Whit Tuesday a strange custom takes place in a town on the River Rhine in Germany. A goat arrives before sunset. It is led by the youngest married couple of another town not far away. The couple stay all day

and watch folk-dancing, and take part in the feasting and the singing. Everyone is in happy, holiday mood.

Then as evening draws near, a great crowd gathers round the steps of the town hall, where the goat stands in a place of honour. At quarter to six an auction begins. Local people offer a price for the goat. The prices go higher and higher. Then the clock strikes six, and the goat is sold to the person who made the last offer.

This is a custom that goes back to the year 1404, and perhaps even further back than that. The town on the Rhine in those days agreed to let the other town use a certain part of its land for grazing its animals. The rent was to be one goat, handsome, strong and with good horns. It was to be given before sunset on Whit Tuesday every year, and it was to be sold by auction on the town hall steps.

This was done year after year, and in 1808 the agreement was written out anew. For some reason it needed the signature of Napoleon I. He was in Spain at the time, and the paper was taken to him in his army camp.

Then all went well until the year 1852. On the Whit Tuesday of that year, the sun rose, and the goat had not arrived. Where was it? It came at last, somewhat late in the day. It seemed to have been chosen in a hurry, for it was not a very healthy-looking goat. It was thin and scraggy. Its horns looked odd and its coat was poor. The people of the town refused to take it.

"It is not good enough," they said, and they sent it back.

Another goat arrived two months later, but this did not satisfy the people of the town either. They were so angry about the affair that they took it to court. The case dragged on and on, and was not settled until seven years later. Then the town that rented the grazing land was ordered to give seven goats to make up for the years between.

Since then, both towns have been happy about the arrangement, and the custom has gone on and on. In these days the goat-auction brings people into the town from near and far to join in the fun and excitement.

4. Goats in France

France has a special goat of its own which belongs to legend more than history. It is the Golden Goat, and it guards an underground treasure which was hidden long ago by the Saracens.

Some people say that the goat appears every morning at daybreak on a certain hill. Others say it rushes from a cavern at midnight on the twenty-fourth of June. Others say it loses its power at midnight on Christmas Day. Then if you are near enough and fast enough you can take the treasure from it.

But where is the treasure? There seem to be many places. It is under certain hills, or in deep caverns or beneath ancient ruins. Many places are named after the goat that guards it. There is Goat's Mountain and Goat Cavern and Goat's Grotto and Goat Pass.

If you find the treasure and do not escape with it before the magic moment ends, the cavern or the grotto will close upon you for ever. If you *do* escape with it, but are really not good enough to possess it, it will always make you sad in the midst of your wealth. So perhaps it is better to leave it with its guardian, the Golden Goat.

The Great Statue

On the edge of the South American town where Pablo lived was a steep, rocky hill, and on the top of the hill was a statue of St James. The hill itself was not very high, but the statue towered up into the sky so that sometimes on rainy days its head was lost in the clouds. The statue faced the town, and its arms were spread wide as if St James were watching over all the people who lived and worked in the streets below.

Most of the people were fond of the statue. They felt that St James really did look down and help them and look after them. Pablo's mother, however, felt quite differently about it, because once a year the statue had to be cleaned, and the person who cleaned it was her brother Manuel, Pablo's uncle.

At one time, four men had worked on it together, but first one had given up, then another had given up, and then another had given up, and for the past three years Manuel had done the cleaning all on his own.

Now the cleaning time was drawing near again, and Mother was worrying about it, and Uncle Manuel was saying,

"Well, someone has to do it."

"Tell me how you clean the statue, Uncle Manuel," said Pablo, for he never tired of hearing about it, and sometimes he thought he might even help Uncle Manuel with it himself when he grew a bit older.

"Well," began Uncle Manuel slowly, "I take water and my cleaning things and walk up the hill, and I climb up the steps cut in the rock at the base of the statue. I stand at the back of St James and I put up my long, expanding ladder, with the top of it resting a little below his waist. I roll some big stones against the foot of the ladder, to keep it steady, and then I climb up.

When I get to the top of the ladder I am within reach of some iron rungs that go all the rest of the way up to the head. I clamber up, using hands and feet, hands and feet until I come to a little resting place in the folds of the saint's cloak. I rest a moment, and then I go up more iron rungs, using hands and feet, hands and feet until I come to the neck and then to the back of the head."

"And at the back of the head there's a door, isn't there?" put in Pablo.

"Yes," said Uncle Manuel, "and it leads to a little room where I leave my cleaning things from day to day." Pablo always loved to hear about the little room inside the statue's head.

"And I go inside and shut the door and rest awhile on a wooden seat," said Uncle Manuel.

"Tell me about the mouth," begged Pablo.

"The mouth of St James is open a little, like a window," explained Uncle Manuel. "I always go and look out of it, and I can see the town spread out below. I can see the streets, and I can see shops and houses and cars, very small and far away. They are so small that they look like the toys of a child."

"Now tell me how you crawl along the arms and scrub St James's hands," said Pablo.

"That is the worst part of all," went on Uncle Manuel. "Sometimes it is so hot that the sun burns my face, and sometimes it is so cold that I can hardly hold my brush – and when it is windy, the arms shake and tremble, and I shake and tremble with them."

Pablo's mother had not stayed to hear all this, but

now she came into the room again and gave Uncle Manuel a cup of coffee and asked,

"When do you start?"

"Tomorrow – Wednesday," he replied.

"The radio says it's going to be hot tomorrow. You'd better wear your red shirt and keep as cool as you can."

"Yes, I will," agreed Uncle Manuel.

"I wish you wouldn't do the cleaning," sighed Mother.

"Well, someone has to do it," said Uncle Manuel again.

. . . . . .

It was Wednesday. The sun was shining, and Uncle Manuel had climbed to the top of the statue, and started work. He always started on the head, because St James had a sort of collar, where Uncle Manuel could stand, and from which he could reach all the parts of the head fairly easily. Besides he liked doing the head, and especially the face. Slowly, carefully he worked, scrubbing the head, the ears, the eyes, the nose, the chin, the cheeks, the parted lips.

All the morning he worked and by midday the head was finished. Uncle Manuel went back into the little room inside the statue's head. He sat on the wooden

seat and took a long drink from his water bottle, and ate
the piece of hard, crusty loaf and the cheese that
Pablo's mother had given him for lunch. Then he
rested awhile, and looked through St James's mouth at
the town spread out below. He saw the streets, and he
saw shops and houses and cars, very small and far away,
so small that they looked like the toys of a child.

The sun was shining on the town. It was gleaming on
white walls, and glinting on glass window panes, and
being reflected back in blazing patches of dazzling
light. But a dark shadow was creeping over the hillside,
and black clouds were gathering around the head of
St James.

"Oh dear," thought Uncle Manuel, "I hope there isn't going to be a storm." He finished his lunch and went outside to look at the sky. A gust of wind caught at him so fiercely that he drew back quickly and closed the door again. Wind!

"I can work in heat. I can work in cold," said Uncle Manuel to himself, "but I cannot work in such a strong wind. I shall have to wait." Now came rain! It came with a rush and a flurry, beating up against St James's face, howling round his cheeks of stone, even flying in a little through his parted lips.

Uncle Manuel sat on the wooden seat inside the head, and he waited. The rain and the wind went on for about half an hour, very wild and strong. Uncle Manuel was thankful that he had not been crawling along one of the arms, or scrubbing the hands of St James.

"I should have been blown off," he thought. Soon the rain stopped and the wind died down. The statue, of course, was now very wet and rather slippery.

It was not really safe for Uncle Manuel to climb about on it now. He decided that he had better go home, and start again the next day.

He left his cleaning things in a corner of the little room. He closed the door and started climbing down the iron rungs at the back of St James. He clambered down, using hands and feet, hands and feet until he came to the little resting place in the folds of the saint's cloak.

As he rested there a moment he glanced down and saw something that made him gasp with horror. The ladder had gone! His long, expanding ladder was lying on the rock below. The wind had blown it down. Now what was Uncle Manuel to do? It was much, much too far to jump from the lowest of the iron rungs. It was not as if there were soft earth or grass to land on below. There was nothing but solid rock.

Uncle Manuel stood a little longer in the folds of the saint's cloak. Then he turned and began to climb up the iron rungs again until he came to the door at the back of the statue's head. He opened it and went inside the little room and sat down on the wooden seat and wondered what to do.

"I shall have to put out a distress signal," he thought. "Then if people see it, someone will come along to find out what's wrong. Now, what can I use as a distress signal?" He looked round the little bare room. Then he thought,

"Of course! My red shirt!" Slowly he took off his red shirt. Now, where should he put it? There seemed only one possible place. He could hang it out through the mouth of St James.

"I hope you won't mind, St James," he said, and he muttered a little prayer. Then he pushed the red shirt through the statue's parted lips so that some of it hung outside and some of it hung inside. Then he waited. He waited so long that soon he fell asleep, sitting on the wooden seat and leaning back against the inside of St James's cold, stone cheek.

.   .   .   .   .   .

Meanwhile life went on as usual in the town below. People were so used to seeing the statue towering above the hillside, that they scarcely gave it a glance, and those who did look, did not even notice the patch of red at the mouth because it looked so tiny and far away that it could have been a scarlet butterfly resting, or a red petal blown there by the wind.

So no one thought about it at all, and no one knew it was a signal for help – until Pablo came along the street on his way home from school. He looked up at the great statue, because he knew Uncle Manuel was up there. He shaded his eyes against the sun and he gazed and gazed, hoping he might see Uncle Manuel moving like a little fly on St James. He gazed and gazed, but he could not see Uncle Manuel.

Then he noticed something strange and very unusual. St James seemed to have his tongue out – a little red tongue. It had *never* been there before. Pablo was puzzled. Then he thought,

"It must be Uncle Manuel's red shirt. Perhaps he's put it through the mouth for a joke – to look like a tongue." But no! Uncle Manuel would never play a joke on the statue of St James! The red shirt must be there for another reason. Now Pablo's cheeks went pink as he suddenly thought,

"Perhaps Uncle Manuel is in some kind of trouble. Perhaps the red shirt is a danger signal – or a signal for help."

Pablo ran home as fast as he could.

"Mother, Mother," he said, "Uncle Manuel's red shirt is hanging out of St James's mouth. I think it might be a signal for help."

"Oh dear!" wailed Mother. "I've been worrying about him all day. There was a storm up there on the hill this afternoon. We'd better tell the fire brigade.

They have long ladders and are used to climbing. You run on and tell the fire brigade, Pablo, and I'll go to the statue."

No one but Pablo had noticed that St James had a little red tongue, but in a few minutes nearly everyone in the town was talking about it. First of all they turned round to stare at Pablo as he rushed along to the Fire Station. Then they saw his mother running, puffing and panting some way behind, and spreading the news in gasps as she went.

"My brother – Manuel – needs help! – Red shirt on St – James – like a tongue." Gradually people in the street began to stand still and look up at the statue.

"Yes. There it is. Manuel's red shirt!"

"Where? I can't see it."

"There – like a tongue. See?"

"He must need help."

"I wonder what's wrong."

People stood together in little groups and pointed up at the statue. They came out of shops and houses and gazed up at St James. They shaded their eyes against the sun, and they saw the little red tongue.

"Clang, clang!" Now a fire-engine was tearing along and all the cars were drawing into the sides of the street and stopping.

"Look!" cried someone. "There's a little boy with the firemen! It's Pablo!"

It was indeed Pablo, and he felt very proud to be sitting at the front of the fire-engine with the driver, and racing along the road with the firebell clanging.

Uncle Manuel had woken up again by this time and was feeling rather worried. The afternoon had almost gone, and no one had come to help him. Wouldn't *anyone* see his signal? He looked out of St James's mouth, where the shirt still hung.

Something strange seemed to be happening in the town. All the cars were standing still, like little toys a child had left. Only one was moving – a red one. Perhaps it was the fire-engine. There must be a fire somewhere.

"I wonder where it is," thought Uncle Manuel. Then the fire-engine disappeared from sight and the cars started moving again, tiny and far away as if a child below had begun to play with its toys once more.

"Hello, hello," came a sudden loud voice, and someone opened the door and walked into the little room inside the statue's head. It was a fireman.

"Well!" cried Uncle Manuel in relief. "I've never been so pleased to see anyone in my life!"

"Young Pablo noticed your signal," explained the fireman. "I say! It's strange up here, isn't it? There's a window, I see. Oh it's the mouth – the mouth of St James! Well I never!"

Uncle Manuel pulled his red shirt inside again and put it on.

"Would you like to go first?" he said. So the fireman began to climb down the iron rungs, and Uncle Manuel closed the door of the little room and followed him. When he reached the resting place in the folds of the saint's cloak, he could see that his long, expanding ladder was back in place.

"It won't fall down this time," said the fireman. "One of our men is holding it firm." Down, down went the fireman. Down, down went Uncle Manuel, and there on the rock at the base of the statue he found quite a crowd of people waiting to welcome him, and among them were Pablo and his mother. Everyone cheered Uncle Manuel. Then someone said loudly,

"I shouldn't think you'll be cleaning St James any more, will you?"

"Oh well," replied Uncle Manuel, "someone has to do it." Then he caught sight of Pablo, and he picked him up and hugged him, and carried him all the way home, high above the heads of the crowd, like a hero. And St James stood with his arms spread wide as if he were watching over all the people, and blessing them.

The Monkey

When Mike came out of the grocery shop where he had been doing a little shopping for his mother, he saw his friend, Jim, on the pavement.

"Mike," said Jim, "come and see what I've found."

"What is it?" asked Mike.

"It's a lorry from a circus. There's a monkey on it."

Jim led the way to a small patch of land where a house had been pulled down, and nothing yet built in its place. A lorry was parked there. Apart from some decorations painted in red on the side, there was nothing very interesting about the lorry or its contents – except the monkey. The monkey crouched in a small cage that was wedged between some iron poles and a pile of narrow planks. She clung to the bars of her cage with tiny, curled fingers. She stared out at the dismal grey city with sad, round eyes.

"Nice, isn't it?" said Jim.

"Dear little thing," murmured Mike. He reached up to the bars and touched the tiny fingers. He spoke softly and the monkey seemed to listen.

The boys hung around the lorry and talked to the monkey for some time. Jim was hoping the driver would come back. He might be a clown or an acrobat. But whoever he was, he did not come.

"I'd better take the shopping home," said Mike at last.

"I'll walk with you," offered Jim. They had not gone far when they were aware of something coming up behind them. They turned and looked.

"Oh!" exclaimed Jim. "The monkey!" There she was, standing on the pavement at their feet. She was free. Mike's eyes grew wide with surprise and his cheeks went pink.

"Oh dear," he said. "I wonder if I loosened the catch of the cage when I was playing with her." He picked the monkey up in his arms. She was light and warm and trusting. She made no attempt to get away. Mike would have loved to keep her but he said quickly,

"We'd better take her back to the lorry at once."

"Yes," agreed Jim, "and make sure we fasten her cage."

They turned and walked back to the patch of waste ground. They stood still in horror and amazement. The lorry was not there! It had gone. There was only a dusty tyre mark across the pavement to show that it had ever been there at all.

"It's gone!" whispered Jim.

"Gone!" echoed Mike. They felt very worried. They were left holding a monkey that did not belong to them. What could they possibly do with it?

In time they would probably think of something sensible like taking it to the police station, or going home and asking one of their mothers what to do – but for the moment they had no such ideas.

"Let's take it to the park," suggested Jim. "Then we can think what to do."

The park was quite near. It was not really a park, but just a square of tired and dusty grass in the middle of the shabby town. There were a few iron seats in it, and there was a clump of tall green lime trees. The monkey had been quiet and patient until that moment, but now she leaped suddenly from Mike's arms. She bounded across the grass and scrambled up into the

branches of one of the lime trees. She shook the leaves and gave little cries of pleasure and surprise.

The boys walked over to the trees. They watched the monkey and waited for her to come down, but she did not come. They held out their hands and called to her. Still she did not come.

"I'll climb up and get her," said Mike, passing his bag of shopping to Jim. He liked climbing, and in a few minutes he was up in the tree.

"Come on," he said gently but the monkey jumped to a higher branch.

"Come on," repeated Mike, climbing higher, but again the monkey jumped out of reach. Higher she went and higher. Higher went Mike.

Jim stood below and gazed upwards. Sometimes he could see the monkey. Sometimes he could not. Sometimes he could see Mike. Sometimes he could not. The tree swayed a little with the movement of Mike and the monkey and the leaves rustled as if the wind were playing among them.

Then it happened. At one moment Mike was calling out a remark from the top of the tree. At the next moment there was a rustling and a snapping and a flurry of sound, and he was falling, falling, falling.

For long years afterwards Jim remembered that day. For long years afterwards he could see himself standing, frightened and shaking, on the grass beside the silent, crumpled figure of his friend Mike.

.   .   .   .

Mike knew nothing more till the next day when he woke up and found himself in hospital. He saw a nurse standing beside his bed. He spoke to her in a small, husky voice that did not sound at all like his own.

"When did I come in here?" he asked.

"Yesterday."

"How long shall I be in here?"

"Just a few days. You're a bit bruised and battered. You fell out of a tree. Perhaps you don't remember. You climbed up to get a cat, I think."

"Not a cat," explained Mike. "A monkey." The nurse laughed and did not really believe him.

"You try to go to sleep again," she said gently.

. . . . . .

And now, what about the man who owned the monkey? His name was Mr Rose and he had worked for a small travelling circus for twenty years. But now the circus had broken up and was going off the road.

There was no longer enough work for it to do. People listened to radio and watched television. They did not crowd to the circus any more.

The animals were sold. The jugglers said goodbye. The trapeze girl went to join a bigger circus in another country. The two clowns started a window-cleaning business in Birmingham, and Mr Rose, the odd-job man, was going to see about working at a petrol station called Renny's Garage in London.

For twenty years Mr Rose had been with the circus. He had helped to put up the big top more times than he could number. He had mended animals' cages and repaired broken-down lorries. He had travelled from north to south and from east to west of Britain, and now after twenty years he had to say goodbye.

He agreed to drive one of the circus lorries to an address in London where he was to leave it with its load, and he planned to call at Renny's Garage on the way. He shook hands with his friends. He said goodbye. He tied his pet monkey's cage firmly on the back of the lorry and drove off towards London. The monkey had been born in the circus three years before and had been Mr Rose's companion ever since. He loved her dearly, and the monkey asked nothing more than to be near him.

Mr Rose found Renny's Garage. He drove past it and looked for somewhere to park the lorry. He found a small patch of waste land where a house had been pulled down, and nothing yet built in its place. He parked the lorry and spoke gently to the monkey.

"I won't be long, Midge," he said.

When he returned a little later he was feeling much happier. The owner of the petrol station was a friendly man. He had offered a job to Mr Rose, and had given him a bed-sitting-room above the garage, and what was most important, he had agreed that Midge the monkey could share it with him.

"So now Midge," Mr Rose said, "we'll deliver this lorry and then we'll go to our new home."

The address at which the lorry had to be left was only a street or two away. Mr Rose climbed up into the driver's seat and drove slowly over the bit of waste ground towards the road.

The lorry gave a jolt as it lurched against a half-buried brick. The monkey's cage burst open, because a boy's fingers had loosened the latch. Midge the monkey was thrown out, and landed lightly on her feet. She made a great leap towards the lorry but it moved out of reach. It put on speed and disappeared up the street. Midge was all alone.

When Mr Rose left the lorry at its new address a few minutes later, he took down his small case and went to untie the monkey's cage. He started to speak soothingly to Midge, but Midge was not there. The door was unfastened and it swung on its hinges as he touched it. It was open! Where was Midge? Mr Rose felt a great emptiness at his heart. Midge was lost.

Mr Rose left the case and the cage at Renny's Garage and then walked up and down the streets in the vain hope that Midge would come bounding out from somewhere. He walked up and down between great grey buildings and dreary blocks of flats. He walked past rows of tiny houses and rows of busy shops. There was no sign of Midge.

Soon he saw a group of trees in the distance. Perhaps he would find the monkey there. He walked on and found himself at the entrance of a park. It was a small park with tired and dusty grass, and a clump of tall lime trees. The sudden clanging of a bell startled him, and he stepped back to watch an ambulance drive away. A few people were watching it too, and one small boy was walking alone, rubbing tears from his face with grubby fists.

"What's wrong, son?" asked Mr Rose kindly.

"My friend Mike," gulped Jim. "He's gone to hospital. He fell out of that tree."

"Oh I'm sorry," said Mr Rose. "Playing up there was he?"

"He was trying to get –" began Jim. Then he choked and sobbed and started the sentence again. It was no good saying "a monkey". He had told a man and two women and the ambulance men that Mike had been trying to catch a monkey. None of them had believed him. They had all said, "Must have been a cat."

"Trying to get what?" asked Mr Rose as Jim gave another gulp.

"A cat," said Jim, and suddenly he started running home. Mr Rose's heart sank. For one short, hopeful moment he had thought the boy was going to say "monkey". But no. He had said "cat".

Sadly Mr Rose looked up into the lime trees. Not a twig stirred. Not a leaf rustled. There appeared to be nothing there at all, not even a cat.

. . . . . .

Three days later, Mike was well enough to leave hospital. His father came to take him home in a small van he drove at work. It was Saturday morning and one or two children were wandering about the streets.

"Look!" said Mike. "What's that crowd?"

Several people and several children were gathered in one place. There were two policemen, and Mike's friend Jim. Everyone was staring upwards. Mike's father stopped the van and leaned out to ask a butcher boy what was happening.

"They say there's a monkey on the roof," replied the boy, "but I can't see it."

Mike called to Jim and clasped his hand.

"I *am* glad to see you," muttered Jim, who had not seen Mike since the awful day of the accident. Nor had he seen the monkey.

Suddenly a man came through the crowd. It was Mr Rose from Renny's Garage. He put his fingers to his lips and gave a shrill, piercing whistle. Then everyone saw the monkey. In a flash she leaped from the roof, scrambled down a drainpipe and jumped into Mr Rose's arms. She patted his face with her little hands. She pressed her head against his chest. She gave little cries of joy and excitement. If ever a monkey was showing love and gladness, this one was.

"Midge," murmured Mr Rose, "Midge." So everything ended happily after all.